Seek and Find
Fairy

Jasmine and the Birthday Party

Jasmine the Fairy is in trouble! She is planning a wonderful surprise party for her best friend Fern, but a naughty sprite has stolen her wand.

With only the magic of her charm bracelet, Jasmine must find all the things she needs to make the perfect fairy party. If she is going to succeed, she will need your help!

Every time her bracelet transports her to a new part of Fairyland, Jasmine's magical charms are scattered.

The charms are:

- a heart
- a star
- a strawberry.
- a leaf
- a flower

Collect the five charms in each place to help her on her journey, and search for the special items on every page. Also look for the five pink flowers from the bracelet in every picture.

Don't forget about that naughty sprite! He has caused all sorts of mischief with Jasmine's magic wand.

Super Seek and Find

All the items on this page can be found somewhere in this book. Look through the pages to find them.

Sometimes the items might look like they are out of place. The naughty sprite just couldn't control Jasmine's wand and he has caused some mischief!

1 Sunflower
2 Cauliflowers
5 Gingerbread men
2 Snowmen
4 Zebras
10 Buttons
3 Mermaids
9 Pairs of socks
17 Purple frogs
4 Teddies
4 Ladybugs
5 Green cotton candy
1 Scooter
10 Fish
3 Stereos
1 Pair of boots

On the last page of this book is a list of things that the sprite has put in the wrong place.

Can you find them all?

A fairy feast

Jasmine is planning a party today,

For her friend Fern – it's her fairy birthday.

She asks all their friends who play in the park,

Can they keep the secret until nearly dark?

But look – there's a snowman – that isn't right!

It's all going wrong because of a sprite.

He's taken her wand and won't give it back.

Help fairy Jasmine get things back on track!

Can you help Jasmine find these items?

1 Wand   **14** Toadstools

3 Rugs   **8** Daffodils

9 Sausages   **2** Lemonades

12 Apples   **6** Rabbits

10 Caterpillars   **5** Teacups

At the sweet shop

Everyone knows all good parties need treats,

Jasmine goes shopping to buy lots of sweets.

There are cookies and humbugs and chocolate bars.

So many candies on shelves and in jars!

Sunbeams and chocolate are some of her picks.

Keep an eye out for the naughty sprite's tricks!

Can you help Jasmine find these items?

4 Jars of fairy dust

3 Jars of sunbeams

13 Mice

14 Candy canes

11 Lollipops

10 Humbugs

3 Cats

2 Plates of cookies

2 Tortoises

7 Boxes of chocolates

Can you help Jasmine find these items?

6 Tutus   **7** Flowery tops   **2** Cows   **11** Chickens

A new dress

The host of the party should wear her best dress.

Jasmine tries clothes on – but the shop is a mess.

What mischief is that silly sprite up to now?

Mixed in with the clothes are some pigs and some cows!

Jasmine looks round all the beautiful things,

And chooses an outfit that goes with her wings.

3 Flowery skirts   **5** Purses   **20** Eggs   **4** Pigs   **12** Sheep

Market Day

Off to the market to look for a cake.

They look fab! Which one should she take?

And why are some of the market shoppers

Not buying, but bouncing on hoppers?

It must be the sprite, who's trying to hide.

Can you spot him near a swing or slide?

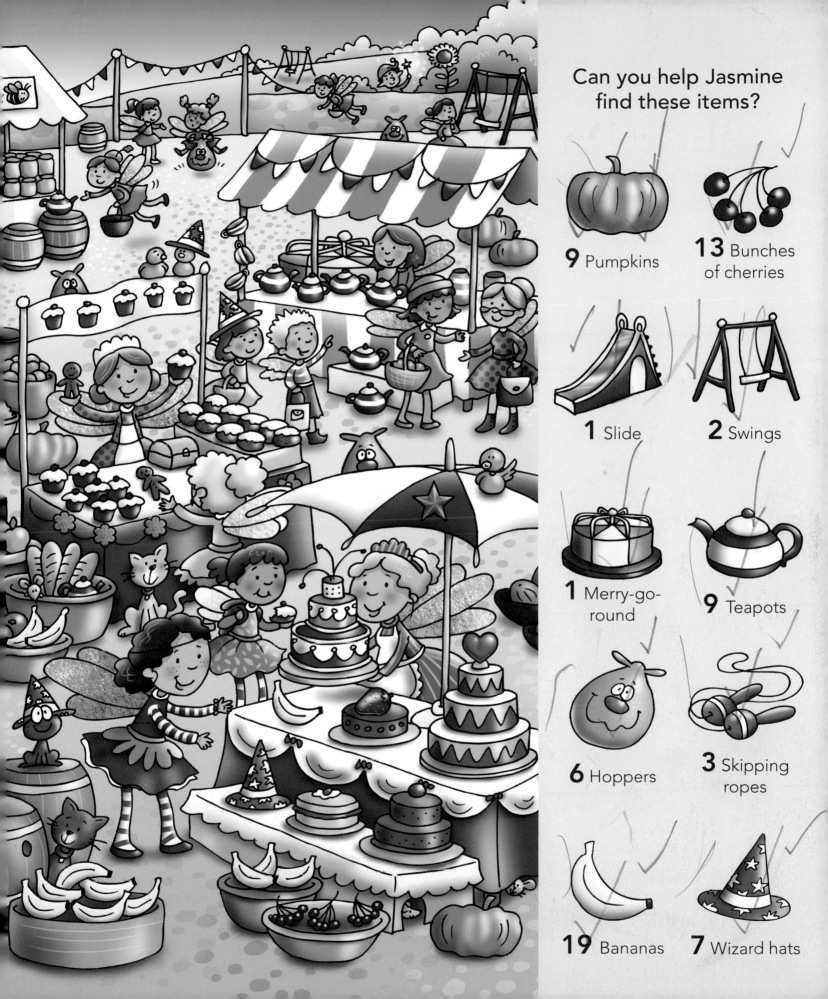

Can you help Jasmine find these items?

9 Pumpkins

13 Bunches of cherries

1 Slide

2 Swings

1 Merry-go-round

9 Teapots

6 Hoppers

3 Skipping ropes

19 Bananas

7 Wizard hats

In the park

Jasmine visits the park, gathering flowers galore.

She has some already but still she needs more.

She sees lots of fairies who all look quite funny.

They're wearing strange hats – even the bunny!

This is more magic the sprite didn't mean.

Can you see where he's hiding, near the ice-cream?

Can you help Jasmine find these items?

5 Silverbells

10 Daisies

16 Acorns

6 Snails

3 Puppies

12 Bees

8 Spotty hats

5 Ice-cream cones

4 Top hats

1 Kite

School time

'Come to Fern's party! You're all invited!'

The fairies at school are very excited.

The teacher says, 'Everyone, open your book.'

But no books can be found, wherever they look.

That naughty sprite has hidden them all.

He loves his new wand, he's having a ball!

Can you help Jasmine find these items?

8 Feathers

4 Flower headbands

7 Pencils

6 Invitations

9 Pens

2 Lunchboxes

3 Bags

16 Hamsters

11 Paintbrushes

5 Pompom hats

Can you help Jasmine find these items?

8 Dragonflies

12 Slices of bread

7 Butterflies

2 Toasters

In the clouds

Once school is over, it's back to the plans,

Up in the sky with the pots and the pans.

What's going on here? Toasters don't fly!

The sprite has sent crazy things to the sky.

Jasmine needs clouds for her party as seats.

She hasn't got time for the sprite's silly feats.

1 Kettle   **16** Spoons   **8** Birds   **6** Sheep   **10** Pans

Can you help Jasmine find these items?

2 Unicorns

6 Tennis racquets

1 Rainbow

15 Tennis balls

In the forest

Jasmine needs greenery to decorate the hall,

But here in the forest they're all playing ball!

Creatures and fairies alike have been caught,

And magic has made them take up a sport.

The sprite won't return the wand that he stole.

He's hiding right there – can you see, in the hole?

13 Squirrels   **4** Baseball bats   **8** Foxes   **9** Owls   **12** Pine cones

Fern's grotto

Fern must get ready so sits in a chair,
Patiently waiting for new curly hair.
She'll star at the party, looking so pretty,
Her home was so tidy but it's such a pity –
The sprite makes mess wherever he goes,
His magic has even changed the photos!

Can you help Jasmine find these items?

 **3** Flutes

 **5** Scarves

 **8** Balls of wool

 **16** Hair rollers

  **13** Cats

 **6** Spiders

 **4** Umbrellas

 **10** Lemons

  **3** Handbags

 **2** Kettles

The wand shop

It's party time soon, but Jasmine's next stop

Is to see Mr Spellikins at the wand shop.

The sprite is there too, to learn how to do spells.

But only a fairy can do magic well.

So Jasmine takes her precious wand from the boy,

And instead of a real wand, she buys him a toy.

Can you help Jasmine find these items?

2 Ribbon twirlers

1 Parrot

4 Glitter pots

2 Sunglasses

12 Butterflies

14 Onions

3 Vases

7 Walking sticks

9 Musical boxes

17 Rats

Party time!

'Three cheers for Fern! Hip hip hooray!'

'Thank you to Jasmine for planning today!'

There's dancing and laughter, cupcakes and punch.

So many presents, and cookies to munch.

They all sing along, 'Happy Birthday to you!'

Fern is so happy – and the sprite has fun, too!

Can you help Jasmine find these items?

3 Flower necklaces

9 Musical notes

4 Fruit punch

8 Cookies

11 Fairy cakes

4 Jellies

9 Keys

5 Sweets

16 Balloons

1 Donkey

Super Seek and Find

All the items on this page can be found somewhere in this book. Look through the pages to find them.

Sometimes the items might look like they are out of place. The naughty sprite just couldn't control Jasmine's wand and he has caused some mischief!

1 Sunflower

2 Cauliflowers

5 Gingerbread men

2 Snowmen

4 Zebras

10 Buttons

3 Mermaids

9 Pairs of socks

17 Purple frogs

4 Teddies

4 Ladybugs

5 Green cotton candy

1 Scooter

10 Fish

3 Stereos

1 Pair of boots